A TREASURY OF
SPORTS
CARTOONS

D'Alessio   Look

"Didn't take him long to break training, did it?"

A TREASURY OF
SPORTS
CARTOONS

Kaufman   Maclean's

Edited by LAWRENCE LARIAR

A. S. BARNES & COMPANY   •   NEW YORK

Published on the same day in the Dominion of Canada by THE COPP CLARK COMPANY, LTD., TORONTO.

LIBRARY OF CONGRESS CATALOG CARD NUMBER: 57-9908

Humor Books By Lawrence Lariar

BOAT AND BE DAMNED!

BEST CARTOONS OF THE YEAR

BEST CARTOONS FROM ABROAD

YOU'VE GOT ME ON THE HOOK

YOU'VE GOT ME IN STITCHES

YOU'VE GOT ME FROM 9 TO 5

YOU'VE GOT ME — AND HOW!

YOU'VE GOT ME IN A HOLE

YOU'VE GOT ME ON THE ROCKS

YOU'VE GOT ME BEHIND THE WHEEL

YOU'VE GOT ME IN THE SUBURBS

FISH AND BE DAMNED!

GOLF AND BE DAMNED!

FIXIT AND BE DAMNED!

HUNT AND BE DAMNED!

HAPPY HOLIDAY

CARTOONING FOR EVERYBODY

EASY WAY TO CARTOONING

CAREERS IN CARTOONING

HOW GREEN WAS MY SEX LIFE

BED AND BORED

YANKEE YIDDISH

OH! DR. KINSEY!

THE ARMY FUN BOOK

FATHER GOOSENAGLE

LIBERTY LAUGHS OUT LOUD

THE REAL LOW-DOWN

FOREWORD

STATISTICS show that the average American is a person of good habits, a decent disposition and an uncontrollable itch to exhaust himself in athletic pursuits.

Millions of otherwise normal characters spend billions of man (and woman) hours smiting a small white ball into the air and then hunting it down through bramble, furze and veldt — only to lose it on the next shot.

Another vast army of piscatorial psychopaths arises before cockcrow to bumble through the early morning mists to some frigid pool, where they patiently offer fancy flies to constipated trout.

Still others bedeck themselves in romantic regalia and venture into the deep woods in search of venison on the hoof. For endless hours these Spartan souls crawl through muck and mire, taking pot shots at elusive deer, elk and fellow hunters.

An average estimate (compiled by the Average Estimate Compiling Company) recently disclosed the startling fact that you and I spend more than two hours a week either as participants in sports or observers of same. This means each one of us devotes more than five years of his life watching the Giants battle the Dodgers, the Rangers lacerate the Maple Leafs, or Gorgeous George play footsie with Horrible Herman.

Since the advent of television, certain sports have become as much a part of our living rooms as curtains, couches and mothers-in-law. The whole family is now concerned with the weekly boxing matches. New heroes have sprouted on the TeeVee screen. It is not unusual to find mother, grandmother and sister Suzie abandoning Errol Flynn in favor of No-nose Flanagan of the middleweight ranks, while Dad makes book on the outcome of the fistic fandango.

Advertising experts, sponsors, television pundits and research bugs have been scratching their collective pates over the strange behavior of women while observing wrestling matches on the living room screen. Why does Mom sit on the edge of the davenport and scream her head off while the Terrible Turk holds the Mad Indian in a headlock? Why does Mom's mother wait breathlessly for the weekly appearance of a wrestler called The Gorilla? And when The Gorilla slowly grinds his rival's nose into the canvas, why does Mom's mother say such things as: *"Murder the bum, Gorilla!"* or: *"Give him a hammer-lock and then break his neck!"*

Psychiatrists are hard at work plumbing the mysterious affection of typical fans for their favorite teams. Through some fantastic chemistry, Little Horace (age two) suddenly develops a possessive attitude about the New York Yankees. In a trice, before the tyke has finished nibbling his teething ring, the entire Yankee organization becomes his personal army of heroes.

Before long, the infant rooter has committed all vital statistics to memory. He will quote batting averages at the drop of a diaper.

Soon afterwards, Little Horace will call each member of the team by his correct nickname, second-guess Casey Stengel and address umpires by such tender names as: *"Stinker!"*, *"Louse!"* or *"You moron, you!"*

Thus, out of some impossible instinct, Little Horace has become a

Porges

Yankee fan for life and neither the ravages of time, fate or a twenty-nine game losing streak will ever alter the childhood pattern of his rooting. He will go to his grave muttering praises for "his team." And he will enter Heaven or Hell with high hopes for next season.

The American cartoonist, a sporting maniac himself, is well qualified to make pungent comment on our national athletics. In his spare time, the average comic artist can always be found deep in studious research on sports — flat on his tail before his television set or munching peanuts in the nearest grandstand. Here he develops the acid hilarities for his drawing board, from whence he ships his merchandise to the nearest publication.

The result of the cartoonist's labors makes up the strength of this book. Here, in simple black and white, the reader will be treated to a bird's-eye view of himself, whether he be an active sportsman, a fan, or a carping critic of our outdoor life. These cartoons, gathered from the leading magazines in the land, are the funniest of the contemporary crop. The normal sportsman reader should laugh his head off, for the collection includes humor out of every popular sport . . . from baseball to badminton, from skin diving to skiing.

Freeport, N.Y.   LAWRENCE LARIAR
1957

W. Brown   Baseball Digest

**"Every man needs a hobby — Gordon's is making a
fool of himself."**

Garel

"Sloppiest track I've ever seen!"

O'Neal

Interlandi

"Ace him."

Boltinoff

Nation's Business

Lundberg

"Step in here and say that!"

"Com'on, Williams! Com'on Williams . . ."

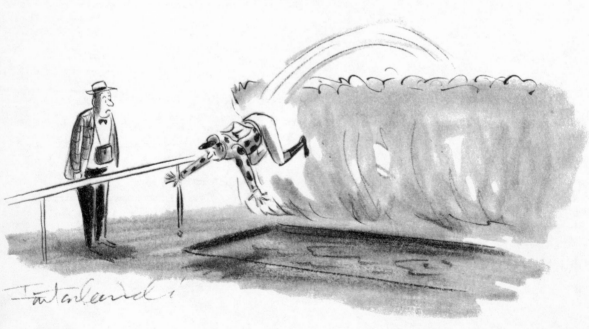

W. Brown   Field & Stream

Gibson   Ladies Home Journal

"And now show me a figure eight, Daddy."

Goldstein

"I sometimes wish George would grow old more gracefully."

Interlandi

"GEORGE HENRY BRADSHAW!!"

W. Brown

"It amuses me on week-ends."

Lepper

"He made five incompleted passes yesterday — at me."

Ralston   Saturday Evening Post

"Here's the picture, folks — tie score in the last of the ninth, two outs, bases loaded and —"

Interlandi

"He threw his first javelin today."

W. Brown

"There's lazy Les Collins, waiting for the tide to come in."

Keate

Publishers Syndicate

"Covers a lot of ground, doesn't he?"

Wolfe

"I'll tell you what's good if you tell me what's good."

Markey

Saturday Evening Post

"Yours is very attractive too."

"Nice try, Mickey boy!"

Johns Saturday Evening Post

"SCISSORS!"

Gerard Collier's

"Are these the best you could get? It's miles back to our car — and the refreshment stand is clear down at the other end!"

"Any luck?"

Wolfe

"It's an old family custom — you have to win me!"

Bernhardt

Collier's

"Attaboy, Simpson. First thing you know we'll be
putting weights on the ends."

Bo Brown

Interlandi

Saturday Evening Post

**"Stay out of this, Hawkins, you're in enough trouble
already!"**

Gibson   Collier's

"Must be someone from the SPCA."

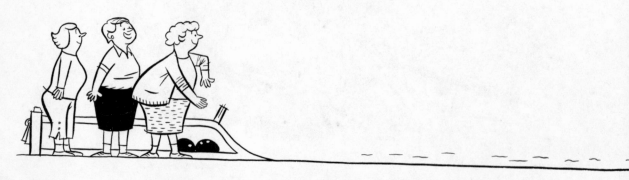

W. Brown

"Alma wins! She threw it farther than anyone else!"

Rodrigues

Hagglund

Army Fun

Lyons

Saturday Evening Post

"You need this for a 179."

Barnes

"Guess what, dear — I have a ball left over!"

Interlandi

"No, no . . . I want that excruciating look!"

Gallagher

Saturday Evening Post

"He's an excellent guide."

Wolfe

"Look how nice she is about letting him go bowling —
and him with a lousy 127 average!"

Ralston

"The pressure on Haskins is frightful. This is
his last golf ball."

Bo Brown

"Drunken diving, your honor!"

Boltinoff

"They claim he's much too old to be trying a comeback."

Saturday Evening Post

"And you call yourself a guide?!!"

s

Saturday Evening Post

"You have to admire her determination."

Partch   Look

"Am I safe in assuming that you'll call that a *ball*?"

Gallagher   Saturday Evening Post

"I'd sure like to see what goes on at that hunting lodge!"

Kenik

"You and your 'Look, Ma — no hands'!"

Goldstein   Saturday Evening Post

"This should prove interesting."

Keate   Publishers Syndicate

**"This is one night my score isn't going to be ruined by
my going over the foul line!"**

Norment

Broadway Laughs

"Hey! Look — we're in first place!"

Tupper

Water World

Markow

Collier's

**"You know the rules of the state wrestling commission.
Now, get out there and act!"**

Zeis

Saturday Evening Post

"I think Harry's caught something."

Ericson

Sport

Ralston

This Week

"Which one of you guys has been fooling with
my uniform?"

Harrison

Christian Science Monitor

Lamb

Saturday Evening Post

**"George is pretty disgusted — he hasn't picked a
winner in a month."**

Bo Brown

Saturday Evening Post

"Dear, were we expecting the Browns?"

Barnes

"Keep hittin' him with the one marked 'L'."

Kaufman   Stag

Keate   Publishers Syndicate

"We'll wager only once, Ruth — they probably let you win the first time so you'll keep on betting!"

JACK MARKOW

TREAT YOUR
DOG RIGHT—
Give him
DOGHEART
DOG BISCUITS

Barnes

Town Journal

"See if you can't make the football team — your mother
and I could use the money."

Lundberg

"Don't you think you'd better take another look at those
tickets?"

Monahan   Saturday Evening Post

"Try not to hit their bats so often."

Helle   Saturday Evening Post

"Does Ike take Mamie?"

BODY ENGLISH

1.

2.

3.

4.

5.

6.

W. Brown

Harrison   Argosy

"I'll let you know if they score."

Yates   Collier's

"If there's anything I hate, it's a sliced hole-in-one!"

"I hit a home run, Daddy!"

"Atta boy, son! Keep it up."

Ketcham   Collier's

"And it'll cost $7.95 for the window."

"It's more than you won, but the extra is
your severance pay!"

"I've never seen the team in an uglier mood."

Shirvanian

Saturday Evening Post

"I'll do the officiating, if you don't mind."

Barnes

**"You skin divers are all alike — always bragging about
the one you got away from!"**

"I'm sure you've heard of him . . . he plays football."

"Harry, I think we're entering tiger country!"

Interlandi

Lundberg

Saturday Evening Post

"We'd like to settle a personal argument while we're waiting."

Markey

"Good heavens! I must have turned right instead of left at pier 17."

Salo

Saturday Evening Post

"He certainly gets into some tough predicaments."

Ross

Wilkinson

"So how did you like bowling for the first time?"

Roir

Saturday Evening Post

"Everything depends on you, Filbrick, so I think I better
put in a pinch hitter!"

Pearson

Argosy

"Miss Feiner, Yoo Hoo!"

Bernhardt

"Set them up in the other alleys, too."

Keate

Publishers Syndicate

"For the last time, kids . . . go away!"

Barnes

"Keep trying . . . You'll get the knack eventually!"

Interlandi

Saturday Evening Post

Harrison

Maclean's

"Well, nobody told me it didn't have brakes."

Ross

"How can you keep a straight face?"

"Looks like the bob sled team has called it a day."

"You and your irresistable bait!"

Partch

Collier's

"I've been *wondering* just why you had a cork in that barrel."

Oakes

"It *is* completed — isn't supposed to have a roof!"

Ericson

Sport Magazine

"Hi, Joe! Hi, Marilyn!"

Norment

"If your insurance company could see you now it would
spit right in your eye."

Baeb

Saturday Evening Post

STRIKE **SPARE** **SPLIT** **IN THE GUTTER.**

Kaufman

"He doesn't know the meaning of fear — or of anything else for that matter!"

"There isn't any hot water."

"I re-arranged the furniture."

Saturday Evening Post

"If he'd ever connected the ball would still be traveling."

Saturday Evening Post

"Quite a large wave, wasn't it?"

"Did you hear that, Edna? The kids call him 'No-hit
Higgins' . . . Some pitcher, huh?"

BILL
HARRISON

"I'm not a pitcher."

Norment

Saturday Evening Post

"Put one in his ear."

Keate

Publishers Syndicate

**"Darn these guys who like to start out real
early in the morning!"**

Partch

Collier's

"It's a challenge, isn't it?"

"Before I married Sam I didn't know one end of a horse from the other!"

"It's like glass today."

Garel

"If you'll help me get it outside, I'll name it after you."

O'Neal

Saturday Evening Post

"How's the new boat?"

Kenik

"Touché!"

Harrison

Saturday Evening Post

"What can I do? he's batting .400 . . ."

Monahan

American Legion

"Dear, why do you watch the Dodgers play when they always upset you so?"

Partch

Collier's

"O.K. What next?"

Garel

"I told you — port is left, starboard is right!"

Kaufman

Saturday Review

Norment

Broadway Laughs

"I'm really not much of a fisherman."

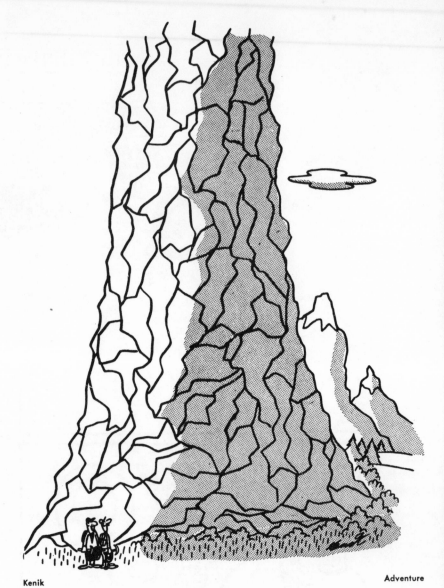

Kenik   Adventure

"Oh, the hell with it!"

Barnes   Fortnight

"Lousy try!"

LOCKERS

"I was robbed!"

Lepper

Fine

Collier's

"That would have been a homer if his mother hadn't made him promise to stick with the baby."

W. Brown

"There goes a great little competitor!"

Beaven

"Look what I found over there — raspberries!"

Monahan

Sport Magazine

Kaufman

Argosy

"Salmon . . ."

Keate

"Getting mad isn't going to help, Lydia."

McCormick   Saturday Evening Post

"For Pete's sake, what time did you tell them to pick you up?"

Garel

"I get better results by tickling them."

Strauss

"A fine time to tell me these things have no brakes."

Goldstein

Saturday Evening Post

"Make it fast. We play Acme Hardware at three o'clock."

Gerard

Saturday Evening Post

"Anyone who gets it over the net gets a point, okay?"

Gibson

"Easy does it, Mr. Follansbee, easy does it!"

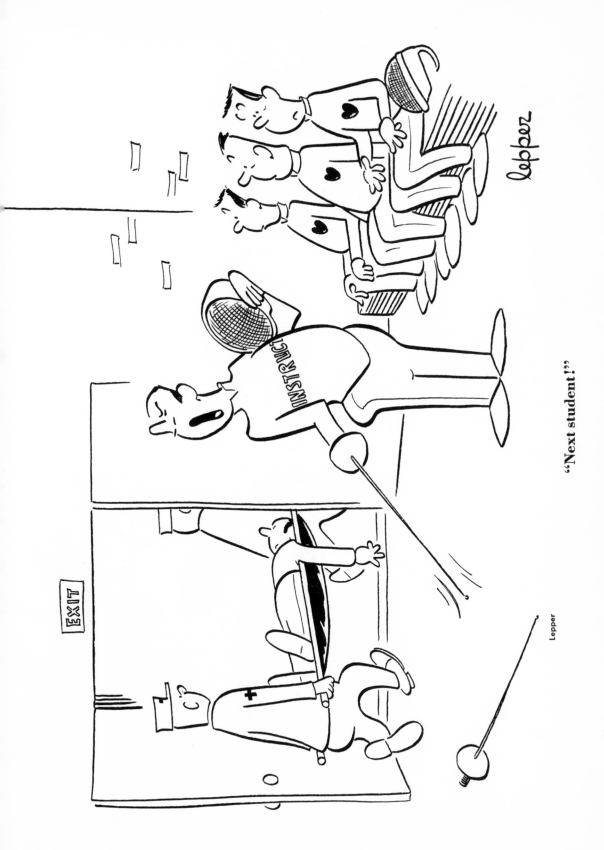

"Next student!"

Boltinoff   Man's Magazine

"—and in this corner, wearing—wearing—"

Partch   Collier's

"Have you ever seen *those* guards before?"

Interlandi

Blue Book

"Okay! Okay! I see it!"

W. Brown

"You seldom see a more dedicated skin diver."

Bram

"We've got an emergency, Doc — I think he's stopped growing."

Shirvanian

Saturday Evening Post

"You're not trying."

Polvogt

"From the noise, you'd think our neighbors run a bowling alley."

Mace

Saturday Evening Post

"I think I'll just chicken out."

Monahan

Saturday Evening Post

"Try a different strategy — like hitting him back."

Wilkinson

Halt

"May I be of some assistance?"

Bernhardt

Real Detective

"Severest penalty I ever heard of."

Barnes

Look

"Be sure to blaze a trail. Then if you get lost you can
follow the empty bottles back out."

Boltinoff

Saturday Evening Post

"His curve is really working today!"

Wilkinson

"We forgot to give them their tranquilizers!"

Lepper

"For a while there it was touch and go . . ."

W. Brown

"Now he seems to have lost his way."

"... and one again ... that makes six ... I thought you said keeping score was such a hard thing to learn."

Porges

W. Brown

"Yup! It's playable, all right!"

Wyma

"I don't care how he does it as long as he breaks 15 feet."

Partch   Collier's

"Pardon me, old man. Your grip's all wrong."

Boltinoff

Nation's Business

"Why can't you be like other husbands who never catch one?"

Wilkinson

Saturday Evening Post

"Gee, small world, isn't it? I was born in Peoria,
Illinois, too!"

"Whatever you do . . . don't insult him."

**"Now there's a real pitcher's duel going on out there
on the mound!"**

Barnes   Saturday Evening Post

"Keep bleeding! The sight of you is beginning to nauseate him!"

Lepper

"You're big, strong and healthy. Now get in there and don't use your head!"

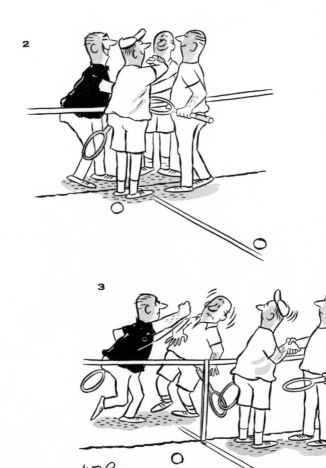

W. Brown   Saturday Evening Post

Kaufman

C.A.C. Journal

"I got *Mrs.* Johnson. Lucky, eh?"

Lepper

"No, No, Hendrickson! *Break* it!"

Goldstein   Saturday Evening Post

"It's personal."

Norment

"Can you stay a while, Freddie, or must you eat and run?"

Kaufman

Stag

Boltinoff   Collier's

**"Gee, Dad, can't you ever take me downtown to an office,
like other kids' daddies do?"**

Hagglund   Broadway Laughs

"Now *this* is what I call a trap!"

Partch   Collier's

Huffine   C'ollier's

"You play a nice game for a woman, Martha."

"... Then I said, 'Well, Mr. President, if you want my advice ...'"

Caplan

Irwin Caplan

Collier's

Partch   Ben Roth Agency

**"Of *course* I want him to be everything you never were,
but must we start him so young?"**

W. Brown   Saturday Evening Post

"Now that's what I call a strike!"

Fine

Saturday Evening Post

"Arnold, you broke a hundred!"

Barnes

American Magazine

"Of course, when I was a boy the ice wasn't so slippery."

Middlecamp   Sport

" — if they can, I can!"

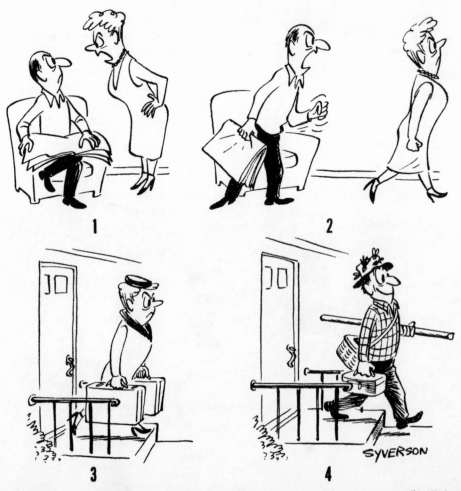

Syverson   This Week

Harrison

"Good old Fred never comes back empty handed."

Collier's

"Understand they paid $250,000 for him."

"Just one barrel at a time, Edna."

Pearson   Argosy

"Looks like your father had a good day."

"Not much of a horse at taking the jumps, is he?"

"Boy, was I overrated!"

**"Baseball's fun when you learn about the finer points —
like balls and strikes."**

1

2

3

4

Tupper   Water World

Hilton

**"Glad we sneaked in here. Someday I'll be able to say
my son played in the Rose Bowl."**

Bernhardt   Collier's

"Yep. Lake's full of fish, mister. Bound to be — no one's
ever taken any out!"

Wilkinson   Saturday Evening Post

"She's not a very good loser."

Wolfe

"Did I ever lie to you? I'm going to work overtime, dear!"

Ross

"He'll make it, but not on his feet."

Monahan   Sport

**"There will be plenty of excitement in the game tonight
—I buried it in the ice."**

W. Brown   Sports Afield

"I hooked a duck."

Scott Brown   Saturday Evening Post

**"It's that confounded overconfidence of his that
bothers me."**

Temes   Saturday Evening Post

"Say, isn't that Mr. Dooley, our bookkeeper?"

"... fencing is a nice sport, skating is a nice sport, tennis
is a nice sport, skiing is a nice sport ..."

"Woops."

Gibson   Collier's

"It's so important for a woman to have some means of self-defense."

W. Brown

"Did you see the pin boy dive for cover again on that last one?"

"Wiggily, isn't it?"

Rayon

"Look, kid the first thing is — relax!"

Ross

W. Brown

Saturday Evening Post

"I used a 10-pound test line, a steel leader, and a non-revolving weedless spoon lure. Then when he got near the boat I hit him on the head with an oar."

Kenik

Adventure

"Happy now?"

Markow   American Magazine

"Shall we have the full-course luncheon, dear?"

Millar   Cherry Circle

Markow

Holiday

"Fast, isn't he?"

Montone

NO TRESPASSING
VIOLATORS WILL
BE PROSECUTED

Phil Interlandi

Interlandi

Look

Pearson

Collier's

"He's not much on form but he gets results."

Harrison   Stag

"What do you think?"

W. Brown

Interlandi

"...got it!"

JACK MARKOW
ARGOSY

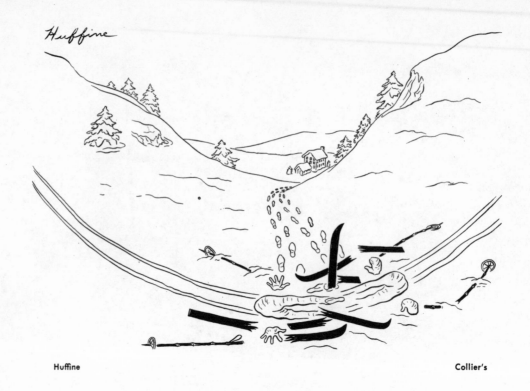

Huffine   Collier's

W. Brown   Saturday Evening Post

"Snap your wrists faster on that follow-through, Mosby."

Ross

"I'm just groggy enough to think I can win."

Keate

Publishers Syndicate

**"Pretty good action tonight . . . considering the game
hasn't started yet."**

Bram

"Now let's go conquer *that* one and celebrate."

Shirvanian

Kaufman

Saturday Review

"Don't shoot, Kensington — I think he likes me!"

**"There's a right way and a wrong way and it has nothing
to do with who happens to have high score."**

W. Brown

" — that shot you've been working out with —"

Interlandi

"He's spotted something!"

Kaufman

Fine

"Say, this *is* a tricky course!"

W. Brown

"What beats me is how a guy can escape from the State
pen and just lose himself in a city like this."

Garel

"And in this corner, may I present Bill Jones . . . no mystery man, no leopard man, no Indian chief, not gorgeous, no golden terror,—just plain Bill Jones!"

Interlandi

". . . then add two eggs, blend well, and bake in a moderate oven."

Sivic

Saturday Evening Post

"Now he points!"

Kaufman

**"Then you take these worms and cut them in half
and . . ."**

W. Brown

"Now be sure to ask him about his skin-diving trip."

Interlandi

Maclean's

Pearson

W. Brown

"Planning to use much whip today?"

Lamb

Saturday Evening Post

"Not much form — but he's held the record for nine years!"

W. Brown

Saturday Evening Post

"It'll fit."

Interlandi

"Seen a rabbit?"   "Seen a golf ball?"

Gerard   Look

"Me? I'd take a nine iron and punch it up there, but
you'd better take a brassie and really clobber it!"

W. Brown

"All right team, let's show 'em!"

OLD ALUMNUS

"Yay-y-y-y!"

"Atta boy, Go! Go! Go!"

"Hold that line, team!"

Fine

"Hadda miserable team when I went and they *still* do!"

"Well, we lost Esther!"

"Atta ole fast one, Lefty, Boy!"

Boltinoff

Real Adventure

HENRY
BOLTINOFF

"Wise guy, eh?"

Brown

W. Brown   Saturday Evening Post

"I think that's the filly from Southern California."

Fine

**"It's a grudge match. Each has openly stated that the
other is more than 35."**

Kaufman

Saturday Review

"Quit worrying — the stegosaurus is a vegetarian . . ."

Barnes · Saturday Evening Post

"How did your long-shot do?"

Keate · Publishers Syndicate

**"They have ladies' tees in golf! Why can't we have a
little advantage in this game?"**

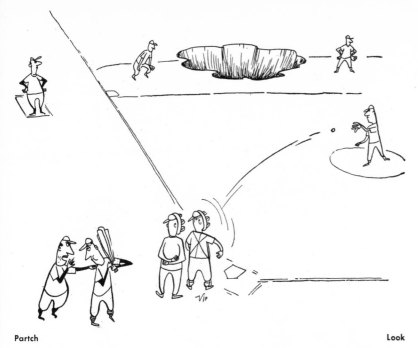

Partch   Look

"Psst . . . hit into that hole between third and short."

Harrison   Redbook

"Quack!"

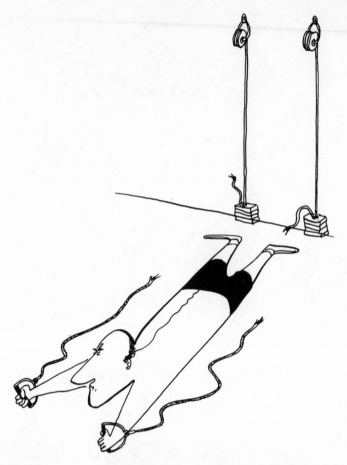

Partch

Ben Roth Agency

Trachtenberg

Wolfe

"Nice return, dear!"

Ericson   American Legion Magazine

"When I knock some down, where does the score
light up?"

ACKNOWLEDGMENTS

THE EDITOR wishes to thank the following team of contributing cartoonists for their help in preparing this book:

Anderson, Bo Brown, W. Brown, Baeb, Beaven, Barnes, Boltinoff, Bernhardt, Busino, Bram, Scott Brown, Caplan, Dahlin, d'Alessio, Ericson, Fine, Gerard, Goldstein, Gibson, Gallagher, Garel, Harrison, Hagglund, Helle, Huffine, Hilton, Interlandi, Johns, Keate, Kaufman, Kenik, Ketcham, Lyons, Lepper, Lamb, Lundberg, Markow, Millar, McCormick, Markey, Monahan, Middlecamp, Montone, Norment, Oakes, O'Neal, Partch, Porges, Pearson, Polvogt, Ross, Rodrigues, Ralston, Salo, Sivic, Syverson, Shirvanian, Schroeter, Strauss, Tupper, Temes, Trachtenberg, Wilkinson, Wolfe, Wyma, Yates, Zeis.

To the following periodicals, thanks for permission to reprint: *Christian Science Monitor, Collier's, American, Saturday Evening Post, Broadway Laughs, Publishers Syndicate, Saturday Review, Liberty, Maclean's, Argosy, Look, Field and Stream, Cherry Circle, Blue Book, Redbook, Nation's Business, This Week, Sports Afield, Man's Magazine, 1000 Jokes, Army Fun, Sport, Town Journal, Real Detective, Real Adventure, Ben Roth Agency, Adventure, Water World, Halt, C.A.C. Journal, Stag, Baseball Digest, American Legion, Fortnight, Ladies Home Journal, Holiday.*

To the following assistants, my thanks for work well done: Linda Lariar, Paula Diamond.

In every case the editor has been scrupulously careful to clear all copyrights and believes that no available permission has escaped him. If he has unwittingly offended against any interests, necessary apologies and acknowledgments will be made.